Help Ma Boab!

WAVERLEY
BOOKS

OOR WULLIE

Hurdles — long jump — funny race —
Wull's training brings big grins.
And, come the day, there's one event
That oor lad ALWAYS wins!

A farmer had no chickens, nobody ever gave him any, he never bought, borrowed, begged or stole any, yet he had two eggs for breakfast every morning. How?

He kept ducks!

Yes, it's a lovely house you have, but why are all the windows broken?

That's nothing serious. I was only convincing a few inquirers that it was a stone's throw from the beach.

I always do my hardest work before breakfast.

What's that?

Getting up!

FUN 'N' GAMES!

Here's Wullie and his chums with the trophies and sashes they won at the Pranny Brae Sports. Can you unscramble the jumbled words to find out which events the lads won?

ANSWERS

TROPHIES: 1. Egg and Spoon, 2. Tug O' War, 3. Marathon, 4. Football.

SASHES: Eck – Long Jump, Wullie – Athletics, Bob – Weight Lifting.

"T-HEE!"

USING EVERY LETTER IN THE ALPHABET ONCE ONLY, CAN YOU COMPLETE EACH OF THESE WORDS?

_AM	_DD	_PON	_NOT	_UART	_RAY	_EER	_OO
_UM	_UT	_EE	_YE	_IR	_NU	_ALE	_UN

_OLF
_IL
_UB
_CE
_YRE
_AK
_ULE
_YPE
_AN
_URE

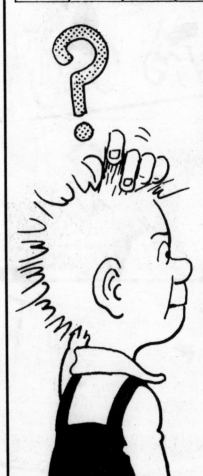

CARTOON TIME

SPOT THE DIFFERENCES!

**There are eight small differences between
these two pictures.
See if you can find them all.**

ANSWERS

CIRCUS FUN

HIDDEN IN THE WORD SQUARE BELOW ARE TEN THINGS YOU MIGHT SEE AT THE CIRCUS. THE WORDS ARE WRITTEN IN A STRAIGHT LINE, ACROSS, UP, DOWN, DIAGONALLY, EVEN BACKWARDS. SEE HOW QUICKLY YOU CAN FIND THEM ALL.

HERE ARE THE WORDS: TRAPEZE, ELEPHANT, CLOWN, RINGMASTER, SEAL, TIGER, JUGGLER, HORSE, LION AND ACROBAT.

A	T	R	A	P	E	Z	E	A	L	O	R
L	A	C	D	E	L	O	R	N	A	R	D
O	B	T	N	A	H	P	E	L	E	S	H
L	O	S	E	G	N	C	L	O	W	N	T
E	R	E	T	S	A	M	G	N	I	R	J
O	C	A	E	I	C	E	G	S	O	T	Z
T	A	L	O	S	G	A	U	R	T	I	A
A	M	O	N	P	R	E	J	I	C	A	L
F	E	Y	L	A	T	O	R	N	A	Y	S
H	O	W	D	L	E	P	H	E	L	A	N

ALL CHANGE

CAN YOU CHANGE THE WORDS AT THE TOP OF THE LADDERS TO THE ONES AT THE BOTTOM, ALTERING ONE LETTER EACH TIME, TO FORM A NEW WORD AT EACH STEP?

BOAT
1. _____
2. _____
3. _____
4. _____
5. _____
6. BATH

SORE
1. _____
2. _____
3. _____
4. _____
5. _____
6. HEAL

WALK
1. _____
2. _____
3. _____
4. _____
5. _____
6. RIDE

CROSSWORD

ACROSS
3. Bird with stilt-like legs.
5. Animal that lives in a sty.
8. Very large bird.
9. A snake-like fish.
11. Not well.

DOWN
1. Small edible shellfish.
2. Remove laces
4. Rodent.
6. To depart.
7. Farm animal.
10. The young of a horse.

THERE ARE NO DEFINITIONS TO THIS CROSSWORD PUZZLE. PRINT THE NAMES OF 13 BIRDS IN THE BOXES READING ACROSS AND DOWN. SOME LETTERS HAVE BEEN FILLED IN TO GIVE YOU A START.

The beach, without his pals around,
Just makes our chum feel blue.
But Wullie's heading for a laugh,
And, soon, YOU will be, too.

If you can guess how many nuts I have in my hand, I'll give you them.

Don't be silly. How can you give me your hands?

There's one thing I can never do without putting my foot in it.

What's that?

Put on my shoe.

IT'S YOUR MOVE

YOUR PROBLEM IS TO PLACE TEN SMALL COUNTERS ON THE OOR WULLIE FACES, THEN TRY TO MOVE ONLY FOUR TO EMPTY BOXES SO THAT THE TEN ROWS INDICATED BY THE ARROWS WILL CONTAIN EITHER TWO OR FOUR COUNTERS.

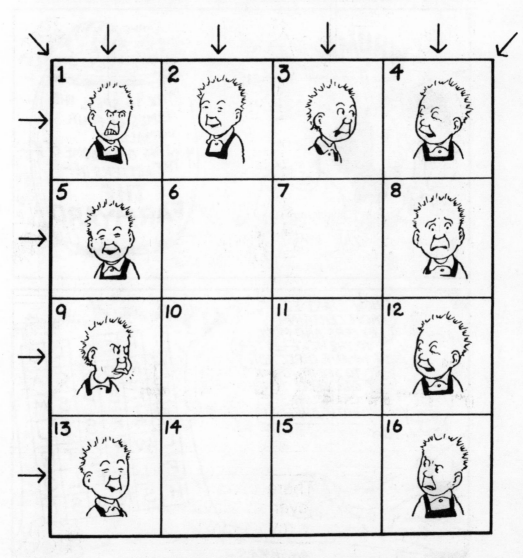

ANSWER—
MOVE 1 TO 6, 4 TO 7, 12 TO 10, AND 13 TO 14.

TRY TO SPELL THE NAMES OF FOUR ANIMALS BY USING ONLY SOME OF THE LETTERS IN —

THE FARMYARD

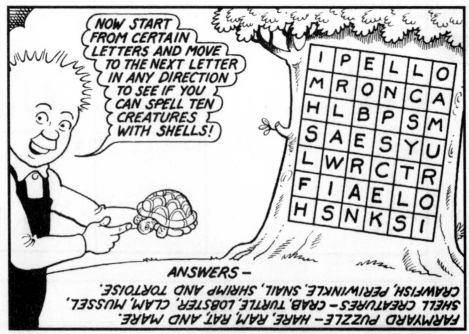

NOW START FROM CERTAIN LETTERS AND MOVE TO THE NEXT LETTER IN ANY DIRECTION TO SEE IF YOU CAN SPELL TEN CREATURES WITH SHELLS!

I	P	E	L	L	O
M	R	O	N	C	A
H	L	B	P	S	M
S	A	E	S	Y	U
L	W	R	C	T	R
F	I	A	E	L	O
H	S	N	K	S	I

ANSWERS —

FARMYARD PUZZLE — HARE, RAM, RAT AND MARE.

SHELL CREATURES — CRAB, TURTLE, LOBSTER, CLAM, MUSSEL, CRAWFISH, PERIWINKLE, SNAIL, SHRIMP AND TORTOISE.

SMART ART

Doctor, doctor, for ages now, I've thought I was a bit of string.

Why didn't you come to me earlier?

Because I was a bit tied up.

FIGURE FUN

CAN YOU WRITE THE EIGHT GIVEN FIGURES, ONE INTO A CIRCLE, SO THAT EACH STRAIGHT ROW OF THREE FIGURES WILL ADD TO THE NUMBERS INDICATED BY THE ARROWS.

2 3 4 5 6 7 8 9

GAME FOR A LAUGH

BOX GAME.

CUT A LITTLE HOLE IN THE BOTTOM OF A CARDBOARD BOX WITH A LID. WHEN YOU HAVE DONE THIS, MAKE A LITTLE BALL OF TINFOIL. THE BALL HAS TO BE HALF AS BIG AS THE HOLE IN THE BOX. NOW PUT THE BALL IN THE BOX. THE BALL IS THE "PRISONER" SITTING IN HIS BOX-CELL. THE IDEA IS, IN TURN, TO TRY TO "SHAKE" THE "PRISONER" OUT OF THE HOLE (PRISON) WHILE THE OTHER PLAYERS COUNT. IF YOU CAN'T SHAKE THE BALL OUT OF THE HOLE BEFORE THE OTHERS COUNT UP TO 50, THEN IT IS THE TURN OF THE NEXT PLAYER.

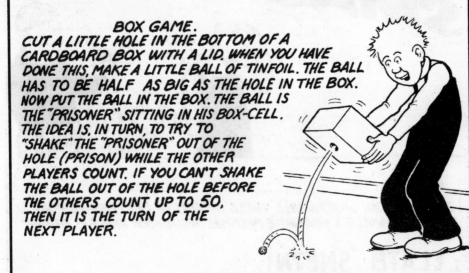

TAPE-RACE.

FOR THIS RACE YOU NEED AS MANY PIECES OF STICKY PAPER OR TAPE, AS THERE ARE PLAYERS. THE PIECES HAVE TO BE OF EQUAL LENGTH, AND THEY HAVE TO BE STUCK FIRMLY ONTO THE SHOES. THE ONE WHO REACHES THE FINISH LINE WITHOUT THE TAPE OR PAPER FALLING OFF, OR GOING TO PIECES, HAS WON.

HE'S A SMASHER!

CRACK!

SEE IF YOU CAN UNSCRAMBLE THESE GROUPS OF LETTERS TO FIND TEN OF OOR WULLIE'S FAVOURITE PASTIMES. WRITE YOUR ANSWERS BELOW!

1. ELATB SNETNI _ _ _ _ _ _ _ _ _ _ _
2. TEKRCIC _ _ _ _ _ _ _
3. IWIMSMNG _ _ _ _ _ _ _ _
4. EDIH NDA KEES _ _ _ _ _ _ _ _ _ _ _
5. BOOFTALL _ _ _ _ _ _ _ _
6. LOUD _ _ _ _
7. NCLYCIG _ _ _ _ _ _ _
8. YLDITDIWNKS _ _ _ _ _ _ _ _ _ _
9. RENOCKS _ _ _ _ _ _ _
10. TAKSGIN _ _ _ _ _ _ _

ANSWERS—

1. TABLE TENNIS. 2. CRICKET. 3. SWIMMING. 4. HIDE AND SEEK.
5. FOOTBALL. 6. LUDO. 7. CYCLING. 8. TIDDLYWINKS.
9. CONKERS. 10. SKATING.

DOUBLE TROUBLE!

WULLIE'S ARTIST FRIEND HAS DRAWN LOTS OF PAIRS OF THINGS — BUT HE'S GOT THEM ALL MIXED UP. YOUR TASK IS TO FIND OUT WHICH OBJECT GOES WITH WHICH.

FISH AND CHIPS, KNIFE AND FORK, BREAD AND BUTTER, CUP AND SAUCER, BUCKET AND SPADE, CAT AND MOUSE, BRUSH AND COMB, LOCK AND KEY, PEN AND INK, BOW AND ARROW, CANOE AND PADDLE.

OOR WULLIE'S FUN SECTION

Jack: "That's a bad gash you have on your forehead. How did you get it?"
Ted (sarcastically): "I bit myself."
Jack: "Come, come now. How could you bite yourself on the forehead?"
Ted: "I stood on a chair!"

Old gent (to small boy): "Well, sonny, why are you crying?"
Small boy: "I haven't got a pond to sail my boat."
Old gent: "Keep on crying and you'll soon have one."

Jock: "Why dae ye aye ask your father tae blaw up your balloon?"
Wee Eck: "Weel, if he bursts it, he has tae buy me a new ane."

Golf beginner: "I always seem to strike the ball on the top. How can I put that right?"
Caddie: "What aboot turning the ball upside doon?"

Teacher: "A biped is anything that goes on two feet. Johnny, can you give me an example?"
Johnny: "Yes, miss. A pair of shoes!"

Teacher: "What is a worm?"
Tam: "A caterpillar that's been shaved, sir."

Teacher: "Your homework sum was — 'If a man walks four miles in one hour, how long will he take to walk 25 miles?' Why isn't it done?"
Danny: "Ma faither's no' back yet."

Sandy's pal: "What kind of car have ye got now, Sandy?"
Sandy: "Oh, a runabout. You know — it'll run about a mile then stop."

"Briggs says he's the big noise at the factory."
"So he is. He's the fellow who blows the hooter at stopping time."

"We've got the safest railway in the world where I come from. A collision is impossible."
"Impossible? How do you make that out?"
"We've only got one train!"

First travelling salesman: "I travel in toothpaste."
Second travelling salesman: "By the tube, I suppose?"

Applicant for job in music shop: "I've a marvellous ear for music. I can pick up anything musical."
Boss: "All right! Help me shift this piano!"

For Wull and his chums, muckle midges galore
Are speedily driving them barmy.
But Wullie's a lad wi' a brain and a half –
A match for the biggest midge army!

Did you hear about the
telephone that fell into the river?

No, tell me.

It came out wringing!

I swallowed a wishbone yesterday.

What did you wish?

I wished I hadn't!

Two-Gun Wullie is looking for Wig and Wam, the identical twins. Can you pick them out from the pictures below?

ANSWER – C and F

TREASURE TROVE

REARRANGE EACH GROUP OF LETTERS TO SPELL EIGHT THINGS THAT MAY BE ASSOCIATED WITH PIRATES.

NOW SEE IF YOU CAN UNSCRAMBLE EACH GROUP OF LETTERS TO SPELL SIX FISH FOUND IN SALT WATER.

ANSWERS—

1.KNIFE 2.PISTOL 3.ANCHOR 4.BLUNDERBUSS 5.TELESCOPE 6.TREASURE 7.CUTLASS 8.SCHOONER

1.HADDOCK 2.SALMON 3.SHARK 4.PLAICE 5.TUNA 6.MACKEREL

Why did the wasp dance on top of the jam jar lid?

Because it said "twist to open"!

How do you know that carrots are good for your eyes?

Because you never see a rabbit with glasses!

PLAY THE GAME

HERE'S A GRAND CRICKET GAME TO GIVE YOU FUN. TWO CAN PLAY OR YOU CAN PICK SIDES. THE BATSMAN PLACES A COUNTER ON THE 'START' CIRCLE AND MOVES CLOCKWISE TO THE SPIN OF A COIN — FOUR CIRCLES FOR A 'HEAD' AND ONE FOR A 'TAIL'. SEE HOW MANY RUNS YOU CAN SCORE BEFORE YOU ARE 'OUT'.

START

JUMBLED LETTERS

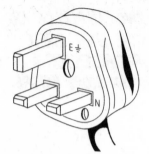

With the initial letters of the objects shown on this page, can you find the name of a colour?

Answer – Purple

JUST JOKING

"Dad, can I go out and play?"
"What, in those clothes?"
"No silly, in the park!"

Why did the owl make everyone laugh?

Because it was a hoot!

What do you do with a sick budgie?

You give him tweetment of course!

What do you get if you dial 666?

Three policemen standing on their heads!

What's the very worst thing you're likely to find in the school canteen?

The food!

READY-STEADY-GO!

SEE WHO CAN WIN THE RACE HOME ALONG THE LINES BY TAKING THE FEWEST NUMBER OF STEPS.

COUNT EACH DOT YOU PASS AS ONE STEP AND EACH STAR YOU PASS AS TWO STEPS. YOU MUSTN'T TURN BACK

THE WINNER

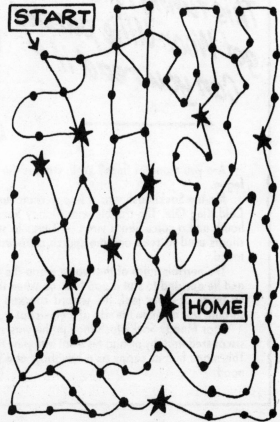

START

HOME

TAIRY FALE

GROODNESS GACIOUS! NELL I WEVER!

This tunny fale has got Woor Ullie puzzled. Can you read it?

Are you mond of fince? Well, stere is the hory of how that dasty tish birst fegan.

Mandy Sackintosh was a happy chan clieftain knell-wown in the days of Cold King Ole. The trouble with Mandy Sackintosh was that he had a muge houth and a soice like a viren — it was lo soud that spenever he whoke the shoofs used to rake and the spurch chire was in danger of grumbling to the tound.

The nerrible toise of that voice made the wocal lizard as had as a matter, and he decided to stut a pop to it. So when the clappy hansman was eating a lig bump of buicy jeef, the wizard sporked a well and Mandy Sackintosh's shrouth was munk to the size of a baistcoat wutton.

Poor Mandy Sackintosh thought he was stoing to garve until he duddenly siscovered that, by micing his sleat into piny tieces, it would mo into his gouth. This made him as sappy as a handboy, and his prince soon moved a fopular pood.

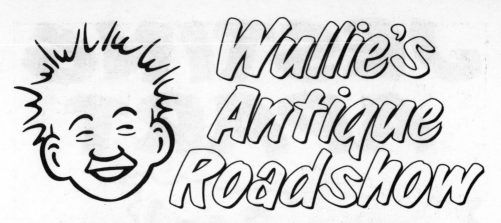

Can you spot at least eight differences between picture "A" and picture "B"?

ANSWERS

1. Radio knob missing. 2. Krankies and Black Lace instead of Rolf Harris on crate. 3. Dent in bucket. 4. DANDY instead of BEANO on top of pile. 5. No label on old bottle. 6. Different date on cartie ('83 instead of '86). 7. 1 lead animal missing. 8. Chalk missing from blackboard shelf. 9. Handle missing from TV cabinet. 10. Bath missing. 11. No ME on blackboard. 12. No BAY CITY ROLLERS on crate.

JESTING APART

ONLY ONE OF THESE FIVE SHADOWS CORRESPONDS TO THE PICTURE. WHICH ONE IS IT?

GOOD SPORTS

AND THESE SIX PICTURES ALL LOOK THE SAME, BUT ONE IS DIFFERENT. CAN YOU FIND IT?

ANSWER — 4 and E

STAR TIME

Hidden in the wordsquare below
are the following ten words connected with the
entertainment world:–

SCREEN
STAGE
CINEMA
DIRECTOR
FILM
OSCAR
MICROPHONE
THEATRE
TELEVISION
CAMERA

The words are
in a straight line,
horizontally,
vertically and
diagonally and
may be read
either forwards
or backwards.

M	E	N	D	O	R	V	I	N	G
I	L	F	E	C	A	M	E	R	A
C	S	O	L	H	U	E	R	Y	E
R	O	T	C	E	R	I	D	A	R
O	R	A	A	C	H	R	O	N	T
P	A	M	S	G	U	M	B	O	A
H	C	E	L	E	E	K	F	O	E
O	S	N	G	R	I	T	I	N	H
N	O	I	S	I	V	E	L	E	T
E	N	C	A	W	D	E	M	A	Y

THE NAME GAME

Each picture represents a well known Scottish surname. Can you guess all nine?

HIDE and SEEK!

Hidden in the wordsquare are eight things Wullie likes to smuggle into his bedroom. They are:-

TELEVISION
SANDWICHES
CAKES
LEMONADE
COMICS
JEEMY
TORCH
RADIO

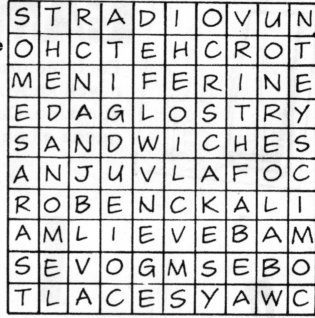

S	T	R	A	D	I	O	V	U	N
O	H	C	T	E	H	C	R	O	T
M	E	N	I	F	E	R	I	N	E
E	D	A	G	L	O	S	T	R	Y
S	A	N	D	W	I	C	H	E	S
A	N	J	U	V	L	A	F	O	C
R	O	B	E	N	C	K	A	L	I
A	M	L	I	E	V	E	B	A	M
S	E	V	O	G	M	S	E	B	O
T	L	A	C	E	S	Y	A	W	C

The words are in a straight line, horizontally, vertically and diagonally, and may be read either forwards or backwards. Can you find them?

OOR WULLIE

Beach donkey rides? An ice-cream stall?
A beach tent selling pop?
No' for Oor Wullie – he'd rather hae
A BUCKET hire shop!

WULLIE'S GONE TO THE BEACH.

HUH! DECK-CHAIRS ARE JUST NO' COMFY FOR SITTIN' ON NO' LIKE MY BUCKET. WISH I'D BROCHT IT WI' ME.

I'VE GOT A BUCKET, WULLIE. YE CAN BORROW IT.

GOOD LAD, ECK. YE'RE A REAL PAL.

BUT . . .

NA — IT'S OWER WEE. I STILL CANNA GET COMFY.

SORRY, ECK. YE CAN HAE IT BACK. I'M AWA' FOR A WALK.

SUIT YERSEL, WULLIE. I'VE JUST HEARD THERE'S A SAND-CASTLE COMPETITION, SO MAYBE I'LL ENTER FOR IT.

HEY! HERE'S AN AULD BUCKET. THAT COULD BE JUST WHIT I NEED.

AW, NAW — THIS RUSTY AULD THING WOULD NEVER HOLD MY WEIGHT. NEVER MIND, THOUGH. I'VE GOT AN IDEA . . .

SOON . . .

READER'S QUERY

GOSH! HAS WULLIE DECIDED TO ENTER FOR THE SAND-CASTLE COMPETITION, AFTER ALL?

WELL, YOU'RE NOT IN THE RUNNING FOR A PRIZE, LADDIE. THAT'S THE WORST SAND-CASTLE I'VE EVER SEEN!

SAND-CASTLE? DINNA BE DAFT—

— THIS IS MY BUCKET-SEAT!

WHAT A HUNK WULLIE IS!

BUT VERY SOON, THE TIDE STARTS COMING IN ...

CRIVVENS! I MICHT HAVE KNOWN MY SEAT WAS TOO GOOD TO LAST.

TOO BAD, WULLIE. COME FOR A WALK WITH ME, INSTEAD.

Do you know who goes to bed with shoes on?

I've no idea. Who?

A horse!

Did you hear about the man who gave a party for his chickens?

He had to cancel it because he couldn't make hens meet!

FACE THE MUSIC!

CAN YOU UNSCRAMBLE THE GROUPS OF THE LETTERS ON THE LEFT TO FORM ELEVEN MUSICAL INSTRUMENTS?

SHOXPANOE	
MORTNOBE	
TINLARCE	
PAGEBIPS	
GIANTERL	
COOLPIC	
PERMUTT	
SOONSAB	
TAGUIR	
ONAPI	
LOLCE	

ANSWERS

From the top – Saxophone, Trombone, Clarinet, Bagpipes, Triangle, Piccolo, Trumpet, Bassoon, Guitar, Piano, Cello.

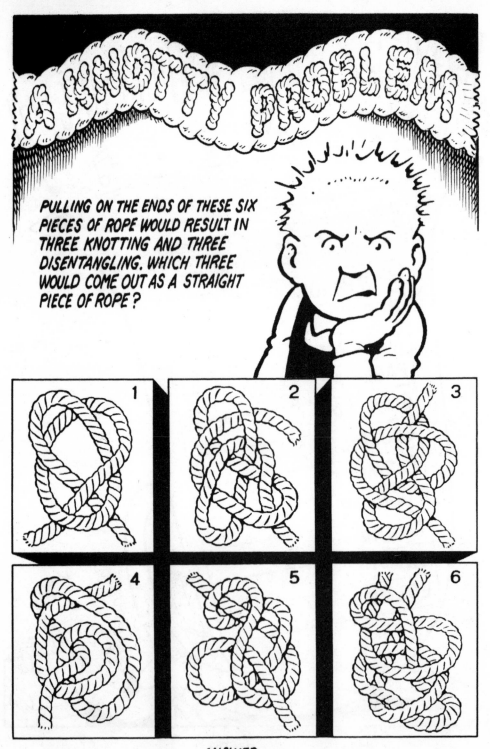

A KNOTTY PROBLEM

PULLING ON THE ENDS OF THESE SIX PIECES OF ROPE WOULD RESULT IN THREE KNOTTING AND THREE DISENTANGLING. WHICH THREE WOULD COME OUT AS A STRAIGHT PIECE OF ROPE?

ANSWER—
NUMBERS 2, 3 AND 4 WILL KNOT. NUMBERS 1, 5 AND 6 WILL DISENTANGLE.

Wheely Good Fun!

START FROM A CERTAIN LETTER IN THE GIVEN SQUARES AND, MOVING TO ADJOINING SQUARES IN ANY DIRECTION, TRY TO SPELL A THREE-WORD SENTENCE. USE EACH LETTER JUST ONCE.

R	V	E	C
D	I	A	R
S	Y	E	F
W	A	U	L
L	A	L	Y

WULLIE'S BORROWED GRANPAW BROON'S BIKE! CAN YOU SPELL EIGHT THINGS THAT MOVE ON WHEELS BY JUGGLING EACH GROUP OF LETTERS?

Why did the boy push his father into the fridge?

Because he wanted ice-cold fizzy pop!

I would like to buy an old TV set.

Why do you want an old one?

I want to see a programme that I missed.

MUSIC MAKING

IF YOU FILL IN THE CORRECT WORDS, READING ACROSS THE TWO DIAGONAL ROWS OF LETTERS, READING DOWNWARDS, WILL SPELL TWO MUSICAL INSTRUMENTS. THE DIRECTIONS ARE GIVEN BELOW.

1. VICTORY, 2. INSTRUMENTS FOR CUTTING MEAT, 3. RAILWAY STOPPING PLACES, 4. DELIGHTFUL, 5. UNITED, 6. LENGTHENS IN TIME, 7. MOORED, 8. A LARGE ANIMAL.

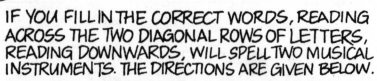

1							
2							
3							
4							
5							
6							
7							
8							

ANSWERS

Musical instruments – Clarinet and trombone.
6. Prolongs, 7. Anchored, 8. Elephant.
1. Conquest, 2. Cleavers, 3. Stations, 4. Charming, 5. Combined,

I SPY

CAN YOU FIND AT LEAST 15 WORDS THAT BEGIN WITH THE LETTER "B"

SHINO TOOTHPASTE

BEANO

BACK TO FRONT!

BELOW ARE THE DEFINITIONS OF 10 FOUR-LETTER WORDS THAT READ IN BOTH DIRECTIONS AS SHOWN BY THE ARROWS. TO GIVE YOU A START, NO.1 IS **BRAG** AND **GARB**.

1. *BOAST* → _ _ _ _ ← *CLOTHE* .
2. *CLOCK FACE* → _ _ _ _ ← *DEPOSITED.*
3. *HALT* → _ _ _ _ ← *PANS* .
4. *BAD* → _ _ _ _ ← *DWELL* .
5. *MOVE IN WAVES* → _ _ _ _ ← *WILD ANIMAL* .
6. *SWALLOW* → _ _ _ _ ← *STOPPER* .
7. *SLY LOOK* → _ _ _ _ ← *SCOTTISH DANCE* .
8. *BOOTY* → _ _ _ _ ← *IMPLEMENT.*
9. *ANCHOR* → _ _ _ _ ← *SPACE* .
10. *PORTION* → _ _ _ _ ← *ENSNARE* .

NOW USE UP ALL THE LETTERS IN EACH GROUP TO SPELL TWO WORDS THAT SOUND THE SAME BUT HAVE DIFFERENT MEANINGS.

1. **DDOOOLUWW.** 2. **EEEHHIRRTT.**
3. **EGHIIRRTTW.** 4. **AAEEGGRRTT.**

ANSWERS

ARITHMETRICK!

WRITE NINE SINGLE NUMBERS, 1-2-3-4-5-6-7-8-9, ONE IN EACH CIRCLE, SO THAT EACH SIDE OF THE TRIANGLE TOTALS EXACTLY 20.

ANSWER

You say your brother is a leading light in the cinema?

Yes! He shows the people to their seats!

Are you sure this milk you're selling is pure?

Oh, yes. Every drop of water we put in is filtered.

ALL CHANGE!

CAN YOU CHANGE THE WORDS AT THE TOP OF THE LADDER TO THE ONES AT THE BOTTOM, ALTERING ONE LETTER AT A TIME TO FORM A NEW WORD?

LEFT

- - - -

- - - -

HOOK

MORE

- - - -

- - - -

LESS

CART

- - - -

- - - -

- - - -

TOYS

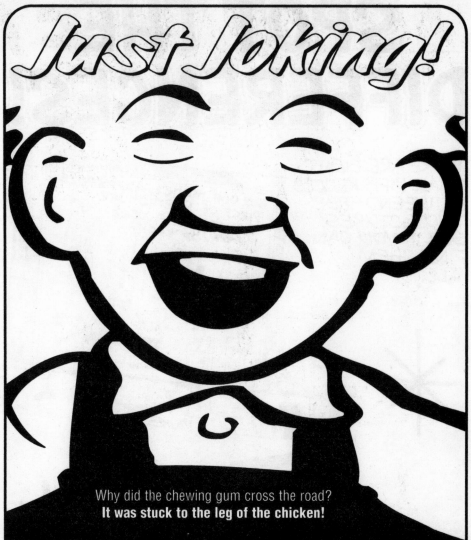

Just Joking!

Why did the chewing gum cross the road?
It was stuck to the leg of the chicken!

Knock! Knock!
Who's there?
Doughnut!
Doughnut who?
Doughnut open until Christmas.

"Doctor, Doctor! I can't sleep!"
**"Sleep on the edge of the bed.
You'll soon drop off!"**

"I've had to give up tap dancing"
"Why?"
"I kept falling in the sink."

Where does an Eskimo pig live?
In a Pigloo!

"Peter, why have you got a sausage stuck behind your ear?"
"Oh, no! I must have eaten my pencil for lunch!"

SPOT THE DIFFERENCES!

THERE ARE EIGHT SMALL DIFFERENCES BETWEEN THESE TWO PICTURES. SEE IF YOU CAN FIND THEM ALL!

RHYME TIME

Here's a tricky test for you. Try to fit in the right word which rhymes with the words or phrase in italics —

Sandy Beech had a big Persian *top hat* called Abdul. Now there's nothing *kitchen range* about a *tin can* having a *top hat* — but in Sandy's *dicky birds* — "Abdul can *River Tay* the bagpipes!"

Sandy and Abdul could often be *awfy mean* marching along the *Morse code* to a stirring *sand-dune* coming from the *top hat's* bagpipes.

"Heilan' *Tea Caddie*" or "The Piper O' *Knobbly Knee*" — it was all the same to Sandy's *top hat*. All the well-known *macaroons* flowed from Abdul's pipes — and they were well *frayed,* too.

Then, one *fork and spoon* about *you and me* o'clock, Abdul gave a performance in the main *curly hair* of the town. Crowds gathered around Abdul and he began to *wander and stray*.

Suddenly, a little *lighthouse* ran in front of Abdul. He dropped his *good types* and chased the mouse — but the music still continued.

The crowds surged around and *stoney ground* a small casette player in the *tattered flag* of the pipes. Sandy Beech was nothing but a twister!

Now ask your pals to try these tongue-twisters:

Six shipwrecked sailors saw seven smugly-smiling sharks.
Six slippery snakes sliding slowly southward.
Four fat friars fanning flickering flames.

Picture it!

Rearrange all the initials of
these 9 pictures to spell the name of
a large city.

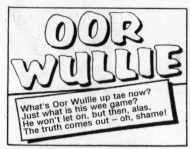

Your face is like a million dollars.

Why, thank you very much.

It's all green and wrinkled!

CROSSWORD TIME!

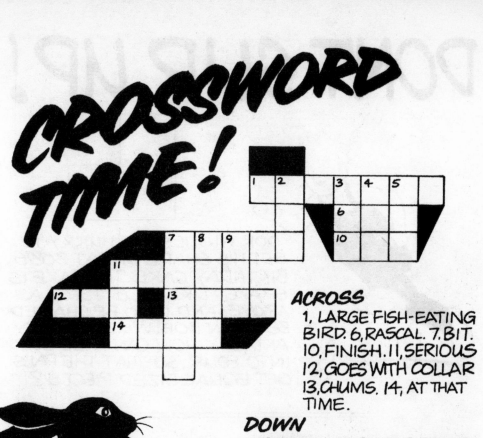

ACROSS
1, LARGE FISH-EATING BIRD. 6, RASCAL. 7, BIT. 10, FINISH. 11, SERIOUS 12, GOES WITH COLLAR 13, CHUMS. 14; AT THAT TIME.

DOWN
2, ORGAN OF SIGHT. 3, FROZEN WATER. 4, TIN. 5, FIND THE SUM OF. 7, YOU WRITE ON IT. 8, RUSSIAN NAME. 9, SLIPPERY FISH. 11, OBTAIN.

ACROSS
2, FARM ANIMAL. 4, A STICK. 5, SIXTH MUSICAL NOTE. 6, WHETHER. 7, NOT ON. 9, TIDY.

DOWN
1, TALLEST ANIMAL. 3, DEPART 5, KING OF THE JUNGLE. 8, FOURTH MUSICAL NOTE.

ANSWERS

Down. 1. Giraffe, 3. Go, 5. Lion, 8. Fa.
RABBIT CROSSWORD - Across. 2. Pig, 4. Rod, 5. La, 6. If, 7. Off, 9. Neat,
Down. 2. Eye, 3. Ice, 4. Can, 5. Add, 7. Paper, 8. Ivan, 9. Eel, 11. Get.
BIRD CROSSWORD - Across. 1. Pelican, 6. Cad, 7. Piece, 10. End, 11. Grave, 12. Tie, 13. Pals, 14. Then,

DON'T SLIP UP!

OOR WULLIE'S IN A HURRY TO GET HIS SHARE OF FAT BOB'S BIRTHDAY CAKE. THE CAKE IS SHAPED LIKE A LETTER "L", AS ABOVE, AND IS TO BE SHARED BETWEEN BOB, WULLIE, SOAPY AND ECK. HOW CAN IT BE CUT INTO FOUR, SO THAT THE PALS GET EQUAL-SIZED PIECES?

NOW HERE'S A TRICK TO TRY ON YOUR PALS AT YOUR NEXT PARTY.

ASK A CHUM TO THINK OF THREE NUMBERS UNDER TEN.

NOW TELL HIM TO GO INTO A CORNER AND, WITHOUT LETTING YOU SEE THE WORKING, DO THE FOLLOWING SUM:

FIRST DOUBLE THE FIRST NUMBER AND ADD 3 THEN MULTIPLY BY 5 AND ADD THE SECOND NUMBER. NOW MULTIPLY BY 10 AND ADD THE THE THIRD NUMBER. ASK HIM FOR THE ANSWER, AND FROM IT SUBTRACT 150. THE RESULT WILL GIVE YOU THE THREE NUMBERS HE FIRST THOUGHT OF.

Answer to Oor Wullie's
birthday cake puzzle

HIGH FLYER!

TWO OF THE KITES BELOW ARE EXACTLY THE SAME. CAN YOU SPOT THEM?

—— AND ——

TWO OF THESE DESIGNS ARE THE SAME. SEE IF YOU CAN SPOT THEM!

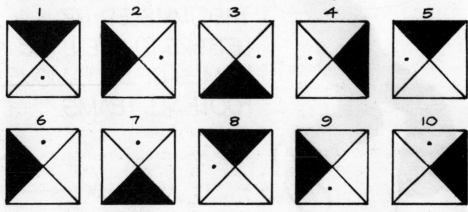

Football Fun

CAN YOU UNSCRAMBLE THE JUMBLED-UP LETTERS TO SPELL THE NAMES OF SIX FAMOUS FOOTBALL TEAMS?

CARTOON CAPERS

Did you know that a scientist has crossed a dog with a tortoise.

It goes to the shop every morning and brings back yesterday's paper!

There's only one thing I worry about in a car, and that's the brakes.

Then you've nothing to worry about – this car hasn't got any.

QUIZ BIZ!

Try this quiz with your pals. See how many correct answers you get!

1. Who ordered the tide to retreat?
2. **What would you be doing if you were "swithering"?**
3. How many red balls are used in a game of billiards?
4. **In which sport are the Queensbury Rules used?**
5. Who created the story book character, "Peter Pan"?
6. **A microlight is a — miniature laser; lightweight aircraft; portable computer?**

7. How many players make up an American Football side?
8. **What is measured in decibels?**
9. Which city telephone code begins with the numbers 0131?
10. **Hampden Park is the home ground of which football club?**
11. Which animal lives in a den called a holt?
12. **Which Scot gave his name to a type of rainwear?**
13. In sports-car racing, how long does the Le Mans Endurance Race last?

14. **What is the name of the Prime Minister's official country residence?**
15. Who created the Sherlock Holmes mystery stories?
16. **A sturgeon is a — fish; old-fashioned battering-ram; creeping plant?**
17. How many hulls does a catamaran have?
18. **Which is longer, the Forth Rail Bridge or the Tay Rail Bridge?**
19. How many cakes are in a baker's dozen?
20. **What is a group of whales called?**

ANSWERS

1, King Canute. 2, Hesitating about making a decision. 3, One. 4, Boxing. 5, Sir James Barrie. 6, Lightweight aircraft. 7, Eleven, plus substitutes. 8, Sound. 9, Edinburgh. 10, Queen's Park. 11, Otter. 12, Charles Macintosh. 13, 24 Hours. 14, Chequers. 15, Sir Arthur Conan Doyle. 16, Fish. 17, Two. 18, Tay Rail Bridge. 19, 13. 20, Schools.

SSH!

HOW MANY THREE-LETTER WORDS CAN YOU MAKE FROM THE LETTERS IN

"LIBRARY-SILENCE"

The ratings are —
OVER 25 – Excellent
20 - 24 – Good
15 - 19 – Fair
Under 15 – Try again!

FOOD FOR THOUGHT

CAN YOU JUGGLE EACH GROUP OF LETTERS TO SPELL SIX OF WULLIE'S FAVOURITE DISHES ?

1. **CRECEMIA**
2. **ILMUDPNG**
3. **SEGUSASA**
4. **FILTER**
5. **GISHAG**
6. **NCEIM**

NOW, USING ONLY LETTERS FROM THE WORD TREACLE SEE IF YOU CAN MAKE UP EIGHT WORDS WHICH ANSWER THE CLUES BELOW.

AREA OF GROUND _____
CHANGE _____
WIDE AWAKE _____
WOODEN BOX _____
NOBLEMAN _____
FARM VEHICLE _____
RIP _____
ACTUAL _____

ANSWERS —

ICE CREAM, DUMPLING, SAUSAGES, TRIFLE, HAGGIS, MINCE. ACRE, ALTER, ALERT, CRATE, EARL, CART, TEAR, REAL.

QUIZ BIZ!

Try this quiz with your pals. See how many correct answers you get!

1. Which kind of communication system uses flags with which to send signals — Morse or semaphore?

2. What is the capital of the U.S.A.?

3. What is a female fox called?

4. Which Swiss hero is said to have shot an apple from his son's head?

5. When was the Great Fire of London?

6. What is a baby swan called?

7. Who was the first king to reign over both Scotland and England?

8. How many balls are used in a game of snooker?

9. What name is given to a squirrel's nest?

10. In which city would you see the Bridge of Sighs?

11. What is the collective name for a group of whales?

12. In which sport is the Ryder Cup competed for?

ANSWERS

1. Semaphore.
2. Washington. 3. Vixen.
4. William Tell. 5. 1666.
6. Cygnet. 7. James VI of
Scotland and James I of
England. 8. 22, including
the white. 9. Drey.
10. Venice. 11. School.
12. Golf.

OOR WULLIE'S FUN SECTION

Eck: "I wonder what time it is?"
Sandy: "Well, it can't be four o'clock yet because Maw said I was to be home then, and I'm not!"

Author: "It took me four years to write a book."
Ex-convict: "That's nothing — it took me ten years to do a sentence!"

"I was born in New York, but I went to school in Scotland."
"Gosh, what a long way you had to go every day!"

Patient: "This tooth keeps me awake at night. What can I do for it?"
Dentist: "You could get a job as a night watch-man."

Stranger: "Excuse me, I'm a film producer and I'm looking for new faces."
Jeannie: "Well, don't look at me — I've had this one for years."

Billy: "Can I have some ice-cream, Pa?"
Father: "No, Billy, it's far too cold to eat ice-cream."
Billy: "But I'll put on my coat when I eat it."

Philip: "I wish I had all the money I've spent on toffee."
Uncle: "Would you put it in your money box?"
Philip: "No, I'd buy more toffee."

Tramp: "Will you give me ten pence for a sandwich?"
McGraw: "Let's see the sandwich first."

"I say, Smith, didn't you say your dog's bark was worse than his bite?"
"Yes!"
"Then for goodness' sake, don't let him bark. He just bit me!"

Dave: "Did you know that in London a man is knocked down by a car every ten minutes?"
Dan: "Gosh! He must be tough to stand up to that."

Frankie: "Please, Mrs Smart, is Bobby coming out to play?"
Mrs Smart: "No, Frankie, it's too wet."
Frankie: "Well, is his football coming out then?"

Teacher: "How many Ps are in soup?"
Sammy: "I don't know, but Ma puts half a pound in ours."

Jones: "My son wants to be a racing driver. What shall I do?"
Smith: "Whatever you do, don't stand in his way."

Guide: ". . . and this stone is where the great general fell in the battle."
Tourist: "No wonder! I almost tripped over it myself!"

Father: "Why didn't you tell me the truth when I asked you who broke the window?"
Son: "I thought my story was more interesting!"

Playtime

HIDDEN IN THE SQUARES ARE EIGHT OF OOR WULLIE'S FAVOURITE PASTIMES. STARTING FROM CERTAIN LETTERS AND MOVING TO THE NEXT LETTER IN ANY DIRECTION SEE IF YOU CAN FIND THEM.

C	Y	R	I	B	O	F	T
N	E	C	B	T	O	S	E
T	R	I	L	A	L	L	E
E	K	C	N	I	G	D	A
M	E	A	Y	G	T	N	I
S	I	L	P	C	E	A	D
A	S	W	I	M	R	T	E
G	N	I	M	N	V	D	Y

THIS TIME, STARTING FROM ANY LETTER IN THE SQUARE, AND MOVING FROM LETTER TO LETTER IN ANY DIRECTION, SEE IF YOU CAN SPELL 20 WORDS OF FIVE OR MORE LETTERS THAT RHYME WITH *SKATE*.

A	R	I	N	R	F	I
T	H	G	E	W	A	T
E	S	I	B	S	E	M
B	L	A	T	A	D	I
E	P	R	F	E	B	N
R	C	G	R	C	T	A

ANSWERS

A boy in my class lives in a sweet shop. Isn't he lucky?

Rather! That's what I would call a real "Home, sweet home".

Where are you going?

Oh, just out for a stroll.

Then stroll about the lawn, and take the mower with you.

IT WILL DRIVE YOU DOTTY!

Counting by 2's, connect the dots in their proper order to complete this picture of Wullie.

NOW SHADE IN ALL THE SECTIONS WHICH HAVE DOTS AND SEE WHAT APPEARS.

Time for a laugh!

SEE IF YOU CAN FIT THESE TWENTY SMALL WORDS TOGETHER TO MAKE TEN LARGE ONES. FOR EXAMPLE, "CLOCK" AND "WORK" MAKE "CLOCKWORK".

ONE	ARM	EVER
MAN	CLOCK	SOME
OVER	PUMP	FIRE
POST	ANY	TAKE
KIN	WORK	AGED
WHEN	KNOW	CARD
WHERE	LEDGE	

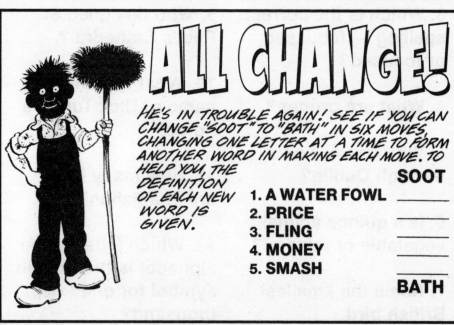

ALL CHANGE!

HE'S IN TROUBLE AGAIN! SEE IF YOU CAN CHANGE "SOOT" TO "BATH" IN SIX MOVES, CHANGING ONE LETTER AT A TIME TO FORM ANOTHER WORD IN MAKING EACH MOVE. TO HELP YOU, THE DEFINITION OF EACH NEW WORD IS GIVEN.

SOOT

1. A WATER FOWL _____
2. PRICE _____
3. FLING _____
4. MONEY _____
5. SMASH _____

BATH

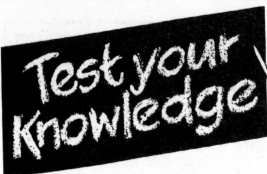

Test your Knowledge

WULLIE IS PLAYING SCHOOL TEACHER TODAY. SEE HOW YOU COPE WITH HIS QUIZ.

1. What is dulse?

2. What are tapas?

3. Which is the correct spelling — focussed or focused?

4. What are prunes?

5. Which river flows through Dublin?

6. Is a quince animal, vegetable or mineral?

7. Name the smallest British bird.

8. How many wings does a butterfly have?

9. Who designed St Paul's Cathedral?

10. What was the name of Dick Turpin's horse?

11. How many litres are in a gallon?

12. Which letter of the alphabet is the Roman symbol for one thousand?

ANSWERS — 1. An edible seaweed. 2. Savoury snacks obtained in Spain. 3. Focused. 4. Dried plums. 5. The Liffey. 6. It's a pear-shaped fruit. 7. Goldcrest. 8. Four. 9. Sir Christopher Wren. 10. Black Bess. 11. Four and a half. 12. M.

J	W	U	L	S	O	A	S	E	C
D	P	C	M	U	R	D	O	C	H
U	T	P	I	F	E	N	A	O	B
N	O	F	C	P	C	T	P	L	U
G	T	A	E	M	U	R	Y	P	I
A	E	O	E	I	U	Z	E	L	K
R	K	B	E	K	L	R	N	E	C
E	C	B	O	A	B	L	D	B	E
E	U	X	D	E	H	S	U	T	Y
S	B	U	C	K	M	U	R	W	S

HERE ARE TWO PUZZLES IN ONE. FIND THE FOLLOWING OOR WULLIE CHARACTERS AND ITEMS:

P.C. MURDOCH, WULLIE, BOAB, SOAPY, ECK, BUCKET, SHED, DUNGAREES.

THE WORDS ARE WRITTEN ACROSS, UP, DOWN, DIAGONALLY AND EVEN BACKWARDS.

THEN USE THE LETTERS IN THE SHADED SQUARES TO MAKE WULLIE'S FAVOURITE SNACK.

DOUBLE TROUBLE

· ANSWERS ·

S	B	U	C	K	M	U	R	W	S
Y	T	U	S	H	E	D	X	U	E
E	B	D	L	B	A	O	B	C	E
C	E	N	R	L	K	E	B	K	R
I	K	L	E	Z	U	I	E	O	A
P	Y	R	U	M	E	A	T	G	N
U	L	P	T	C	P	C	F	O	N
B	O	A	B	N	E	F	I	P	T	U
H	C	O	D	R	U	M	C	P	D
C	E	S	A	O	S	L	U	W	J

WULLIE'S FAVOURITE SNACK – Jeely Piece

Did you open both windows in your room, as I told you to do?

Well, Doctor, not exactly. You see, there is only one window, so I opened it twice.

I hear you had detention at school today. Why was that?

Teacher told us to write an essay on laziness, and I sent in a blank sheet.

TWO THE SAME

TWO OF THESE PICTURES OF OOR WULLIE ARE
EXACTLY THE SAME. CAN YOU FIND THEM?

ANSWERS — I AND C.

Wish you were THERE?

WULLIE'S RELAXING BY THE SEA-
SIDE — AND HE'S THINKING OF
OTHER FARAWAY HOLIDAY PLACES.
CAN YOU UNSCRAMBLE THE
MIXED-UP PLACES?
THEN TRY TO FIND SIX SPADES
HIDDEN IN THE PICTURE.

ANSWER :—
FLORIDA, GREECE, SPAIN, MOROCCO,
CORSICA, CORFU, CALIFORNIA, FRANCE,
TURKEY, CYPRUS, SARDINIA, CRETE.

AIOFLRD	ARICLAIFNO
ECRGEE	CEFANR
NAPIS	YKTEUR
OMCROOC	PSYRUC
CRAIOSC	NIIDSRAA
FUOCR	RCTEE

CARTOON TIME

Find the objects!

BEGINNING WITH 'C'

HOW MANY WORDS BEGINNING WITH THE LETTER 'C' CAN YOU FIND IN THIS PICTURE?

I got this cup for running.

Oh! Who did you beat?

The owner, four policemen, and a crowd of sixty men.

What animals eat less that any others?

Moths, because they only eat holes in things.

Rhyme TIME

ADD THE MISSING WORDS TO COMPLETE THESE RHYMES ABOUT WULLIE.

WHEN HE'S HUNGRY WULLIE REALLY LADLES INTAE BREAD AN' _____

WULLIE AYE GOES THROUGH THE KNEES O' HIS HARD-WORKED _____

A COMFY CHAIR? AWAY AN' CHUCK IT. HE'D RATHER HAVE HIS TRUSTY _____

SOAPY, BOAB OR WEE ECK? NA! HIS BEST PALS ARE HIS _____ AN' _____

HE'S MISSIN' 'COS IT'S TIME FOR BED. BET HE'S HIDIN' IN HIS _____

THEY'RE GOOD AS GOLD IN WULLIE'S STREET WHEN P.C. MURDOCH'S ON THE _____

ANSWERS: DUNGAREES. JEELY. BUCKET. MA. PA. SHED. BEAT.

THE SPOT BUCKETS!

THERE SHOULD BE 6 BUCKETS IN THIS PICTURE, BUT THE ARTIST HASN'T DRAWN THEM YET. SEE IF YOU CAN WORK OUT WHERE THEY SHOULD BE.

FISHY BUSINESS!

HERE'S A TRICKY QUESTION. TO WHICH OF THE FIVE NUMBERED DRAWINGS DOES THE NEGATIVE IN THE TOP LEFT-HAND CORNER BELONG? REMEMBER, WHITE IS BLACK ON A NEGATIVE AND BLACK IS WHITE!

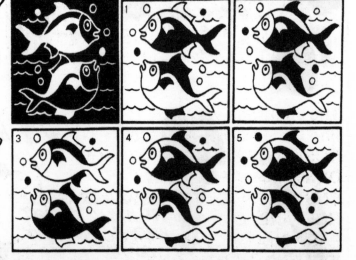

ANSWER   FISHY BUSINESS – NO. 4

The Name Game

Hidden in this wordsquare are the names of some of the countries which have taken part in the World Cup over the years.

N	I	G	E	R	I	A	N	I	H	C	R
O	Z	R	D	S	C	O	T	L	A	N	D
R	D	E	N	M	A	R	K	D	A	L	E
W	D	E	H	D	N	A	L	E	R	I	N
A	I	C	Y	N	A	M	R	E	G	T	G
A	Y	D	E	L	P	E	O	Z	B	E	P	L
W	N	T	U	R	K	E	Y	R	N	O	A
R	A	B	C	H	I	L	E	A	T	L	N
U	L	L	T	N	W	T	S	Z	I	A	D
G	L	R	E	Q	X	E	A	I	N	N	C
Z	O	R	U	S	S	I	A	L	A	D	X
N	H	P	A	R	A	G	U	A	Y	M	J

The countries you have to find are:– NIGERIA, CHINA, NORWAY, GREECE, SCOTLAND, DENMARK, ARGENTINA, ENGLAND, GERMANY, TURKEY, HOLLAND, CHILE, ITALY, PARAGUAY, POLAND, WALES, IRELAND, NORTH KOREA, RUSSIA, BRAZIL

DOGGONE!

TRUST WULLIE TAE GET THINGS A' MESSED UP WHEN HE TAK'S THE NEIGHBOURS' DOGS OOT FOR A WALK! CAN YOU UNSCRAMBLE EACH GROUP OF LETTERS TO FORM SIX BREEDS OF DOGS?

LADMINATA
LOBARDAR
GIRCO
LOLICE
RITERERVE
LATSAINA

NOW TRY TO SPELL AT LEAST FIFTEEN THREE-LETTER WORDS, USING ONLY THE LETTERS IN

SPANIEL

OOR WULLIE'S FUN SECTION

"What does a mouse eat for breakfast?"
"Mice krispies!"

"What do you get when you cross a chicken with a waiter?"
"A hen that lays tables!"

"Heard about the cat that fell into a bowl of starch?"
"It was scared stiff!"

"Why did the burglar cut the legs off the bed?"
"Because he wanted to lie low for a while!"

"How do Red Indians send secret messages?"
"They use smokeless fuel!"

"What can't you eat for lunch or dinner?"
"Your breakfast!"

"What is a snail?"
"A worm wearing a crash helmet!"

"How does a pixie eat?"
"By goblin!"

"What happened to the man who couldn't tell putty from porridge?"
"All his windows fell out!"

"Did you hear about the man who made a wooden car with a wooden engine?"
"It wooden go!"

"What do you get if you dial 666?"
"The Australian police!"

Patient — "Doctor, I keep losing my memory."
Doctor — "When did this start?"
Patient — "When did what start?"

"What did the wig say when it was blowing along the street?"
"I'm off my head!"

"If you cross a dog with a cat, what do you get?"
"An animal which chases itself!"

"One mouse collapsed, so what did the other mouse do?"
"He used mouse-to-mouse resuscitation!"

"How did the man feel when he was run over by a steam roller?"
"Flattered!"

"What do you call two spiders who have just got married?"
"Newly-webs!"

"What do gorillas sing at Christmas?"
"Jungle bells! Jungle bells!"

"What is the best way to light a fire with two objects?"
"Make sure one is a match!"

"What do you call a man who can chop down twenty trees a day?"
"A good feller!"

"Why do bees have sticky hair?"
"Because they use honey combs!"

SPOT THE DIFFERENCES

There are eight differences
between these two pictures. See if you
can find them all.